HOUGHTON MIFFLIN
Reading
A Legacy of Literacy

Voyagers

HOUGHTON MIFFLIN

BOSTON • MORRIS PLAINS, NJ

California • Colorado • Georgia • Illinois • New Jersey • Texas

Design, Art Management and Page Production: Kirchoff/Wohlberg, Inc.

ILLUSTRATION CREDITS
4-21 Marni Backer. 22-39 Gail Piazza. 40-57 S. Saelig Gallagher.

PHOTOGRAPHY CREDITS
40 (bkgd), PhotoDisc.

Printed in U.S.A.

ISBN: 0-618-04394-2

456789-VH-05 04 03 02 01

Contents

The Golden Land

by Lee S. Justice
illustrated by Marni Backer

Strategy Focus

Samuel and his family are on their way
to America. As you read, ask yourself
questions about their trip.

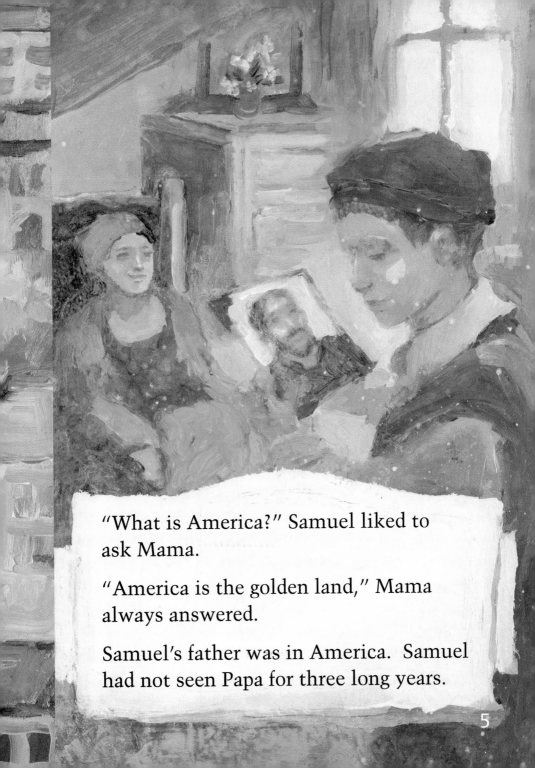

"What is America?" Samuel liked to ask Mama.

"America is the golden land," Mama always answered.

Samuel's father was in America. Samuel had not seen Papa for three long years.

Samuel remembered Papa's hugs and the soft feeling of his beard. Papa was working in America. He was saving money so that he could bring his family to the golden land.

One day, a letter came. Papa had sent the tickets at last!

Mama cried. Grandmother cried. Samuel
cried. Even Samuel's older brother, Myer,
wiped tears from his face.

They were all happy. Yet there was an
empty feeling, too. Grandmother was
not coming with them.

A wagon took the travelers to the train.
Samuel watched the family's house get
smaller and smaller. Then the road curved.
The house was gone.

Samuel had always wanted to ride on a train. It was bumpier and noisier than he had thought it would be.

The houses and fields came, then went. At last, the train reached a busy port.

First, all the travelers were checked for signs of sickness. "Only healthy people go to America," Myer said.

The ship looked even grander than the one in the postcard Papa had sent. Samuel felt proud to climb aboard.

During the long boat ride, Samuel played tag on the deck and listened to people talking. They spoke all kinds of languages. Samuel liked to listen to the strange sounds.

Samuel felt lucky that he did not get seasick like Myer. "Ooooh," poor Myer moaned. Mama held Myer's head.

They slept below with many other passengers. It was stuffy and smelled bad.

"Soon we will be in America," Mama said over and over.

On the tenth day, everyone ran to the top deck. "Look!" they shouted. "There she is!" People cheered and wept.

A man picked Samuel up so he could see. Samuel blinked at the golden sunlight gleaming off the statue's crown.

"She is welcoming us," Mama said softly.

A ferry took them to a big building. Inside were so many people! Samuel held onto Mama's coat as if he were a little boy.

They waited in line. Men put chalk marks on people's coats. A chalk mark might mean that someone was ill and would have to stay there until he or she got better.

"Look strong and healthy!" Mama said. Samuel pushed his chest out. Myer stood tall. No chalk marks!

15

16

They waited in line. They waited on benches. Samuel hopped on one foot. Then he hopped on the other. So much waiting!

When their name was called, Mama would have to answer questions. Samuel helped her get ready.

17

At last, Mama's turn came. She answered
the questions. Then a man pointed her to
a stairway.

"We are in America now," Mama said with
a smile. Samuel realized that Mama had not
smiled for a very long time.

They reached the bottom of the stairs.

"There he is!" cried Mama.

"Papa!" shouted Myer.

Papa looked different now. But his hug
felt just the way Samuel remembered it.

Think About the Selection

1 How long has it been since Samuel last saw his father?

2 Why do you think the people cheered and wept when they saw the Statue of Liberty?

Making Inferences

Copy this chart on a piece of paper. Read each story clue, and write the inference it suggests.

Story Clue	Inference
Samuel held onto Mama's coat as if he were a little boy.	Samuel was a little scared.
Samuel realized that Mama had not smiled for a very long time.	?
Papa looked different now. But his hug felt the same to Samuel.	?

BROTHERS are FOREVER

by Marcy Haber
illustrated by Gail Piazza

Strategy Focus

Max visits his brother at college in England. As you read, **predict** what will happen during the visit.

"Yahoo!" Max shouted. "We're going to London! I can't wait to see Russ."

It was a long trip from New York to London. Max could not sit still. He had so much to tell his older brother. It had been four whole months since they had seen each other. Would Russ even know who he was? Max had gotten a lot taller.

At last the plane landed. Russ was there to meet his family.

"Hey, Peanut!" Russ yelled to Max. Max had always hated being called Peanut. But this time he didn't mind. Russ had missed him. Max could tell.

"I have so much to show you," said Russ. He spoke with an accent. "Wait till you meet my college chums!"

"Chums?" thought Max.

They drove to Russ's school. They passed
quiet villages and small farms.

"It's beautiful!" Max's parents said.

Max said, "The cows are smelly."

"It's funny to see the cars driving down the wrong side of the street!" Max's parents said with a laugh.

Max said, "I think it's stupid."

Russ started getting mad. "It isn't stupid, Max," he answered. "It's just different."

"Your accent is different *and* stupid," Max said under his breath.

28

They stopped at a large stone building.
"This is where I live," said Russ.

His parents said, "It looks like a castle!"

Max shrugged.

They walked to Russ's room. "This is my flatmate, Ian," said Russ.

"He doesn't look flat to me," Max said.

"In London, an apartment is called a *flat*," Russ told him.

"Russ and I play football together," Ian said. "He tells me you're not bad at it, either."

"Russ doesn't play football! And neither do I! We play soccer," Max answered.

"In England, football *is* soccer," said Ian.

Max felt as if he were on another planet.

Russ showed his family around the college. He stopped to talk to his new friends. He kept using strange words. "Jolly good!" he'd say, or "Right-o!"

"Dumb-o," Max said to himself.

Later, they went to Russ's football game.
Russ scored a goal. The crowd cheered.

"Russ is doing great in school," thought Max.
"He won't ever want to come home."

After the game, Max's family rode on a tour bus.
They saw the sights of London.

Max read his comic book.

"What's wrong, Max?" asked Russ.
"I thought you would love England."

At first, Max said nothing. Then he blurted out, "You used to be *my* roommate. Now you have a flatmate. You're a soccer hero. Or a football hero. Or whatever. And you talk funny! You don't need a brother anymore."

Then he added, "And why did you stop calling me Peanut and start calling me Max?"

"I do have new friends," said Russ. "And I do like it here. But you're wrong about not needing you. Brothers are forever. Even when they get too tall to be called Peanut."

"You mean it?" asked Max.

"Of course," said Russ. "And another thing. Ian and I are running a football camp here this summer. I mean soccer camp. Well, you know. Mom and Dad said it's okay for you to come. But I guess you don't like it here."

"Sure I do!" Max said. "That'd be great!
I mean, jolly good!"

Responding

Think About the Selection

1 Where did Max and his parents go to visit Russ?

2 Did Max like how Russ had changed? Why?

What Do You Predict?

Copy this web on a piece of paper. Read the prediction. Then write details from the story that support it.

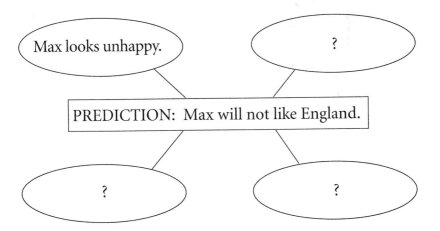

Max looks unhappy.

?

PREDICTION: Max will not like England.

?

?

Iceberg Rescue

by Sarah Amada
illustrated by S. Saelig Gallagher

Strategy Focus

How can an iceberg help Louise free her ship? As you read, **monitor** your understanding and reread to **clarify** details.

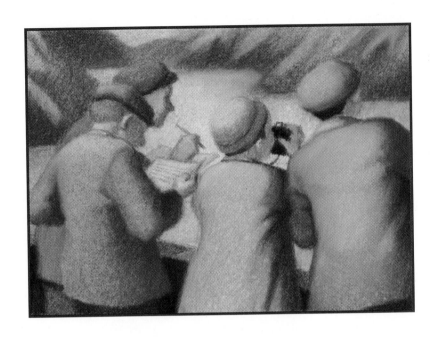

World of Ice

It was the winter of 1933. Explorer Louise Arner Boyd and her team had been at sea for six weeks. They were taking pictures and making maps of the wild and dangerous coast of northeast Greenland.

Their ship, the *Veslekari*, moved slowly toward
Nunatak Glacier. Louise stared up at the
mountain of ice.

She took many photos and wrote down every detail she saw. All her information would be very useful for understanding this mysterious part of the world.

Stuck!

All at once, the ship shook. The shock threw
Louise and the others to their knees. The front
of the ship made a loud sound. The *Veslekari*
had run aground.

The captain yelled, "Reverse the engines!"
The ship's crew ran the motors at full speed.
But the *Veslekari* did not move.

No Way Out

Now they were stuck, and it was the middle of winter. Louise knew that northeast Greenland was not a good place to spend a winter. Many explorers had died here, cold and hungry.

Louise also knew that there were no other ships close by. She and her team had to save themselves.

The tide was getting lower. As the water level around the boat sank farther and farther, Louise waited and watched. She was worried. She knew that the ship might tip to one side in the mud. If it tipped over, the ship's crew would not be able to lift it. The *Veslekari* was very, very heavy.

Luckily, the ship stayed upright in the mud. But it was still stuck.

Time for Action

The *Veslekari* was too heavy to float off the mud, even when the tide came back up and water again surrounded the ship. Louise and the others had to make it lighter.

They took three small boats off the ship. Then they took off almost four tons of oil and gas. Finally, they threw fifteen tons of coal overboard.

Louise's Big Idea

The tide came in and went out again.
The *Veslekari* was still stuck.

Then Louise saw a big iceberg floating toward the ship. She had an idea.

The ship's crew tied a cable around the iceberg. Then they pulled on the cable. The cable pulled on the iceberg.

Free!

The captain ordered his crew to start the ship's engines. What a noise! The motors roared. The crank squeaked as it pulled on the cable. The ship lifted off the mud! Thanks to Louise's good idea, the *Veslekari* was free!

The water around them was filled with ice.
After three tries they broke through the ice and
moved out to sea.

Louise took more photos as they pulled away from the mountains of ice. She was relieved to be free, but she knew she would be back to explore this place again.

Responding

Think About the Selection

1 What was Louise Arner Boyd doing near the coast of northeast Greenland?

2 What is a good way to understand how *Iceberg Rescue* is organized?

Text Organizers

A heading gives information about part of a story. Copy this chart on a piece of paper. Then write the heading to go with each picture.

What's in the Picture?	Heading
Louise Arner Boyd watching the icy coastline	World of Ice
a ship stuck in the mud	?
the crew looking happy as the ship breaks free of the ice	?